Keeping Score

by Margie Burton, Cathy French, and Tammy Jones

I like to go with my friend to play games on the weekend. We like to play many kinds of games. We keep score to see who wins.

Here we are playing golf.
I like hitting the ball
again and again. I want
to get the best score.
My friend wants to get
the best score, too. We
will both play our best.

HOLE	1	2	3	4	5	6	7	8	9	TOTAL
TOM	3	3	3	3	3	2	3	2	3	25
SUE	3	3	4	4	2	2	3	3	4	28

My friend and I like playing baseball. We like to go into the batting cage to hit the ball. We both try to get the best score by hitting the most balls.

SUE   3
_____

TOM   2

Now, we will go bowling.
I like bowling because
you hit the pins with the ball
again and again.
We both want to get
the best score by bringing
down the most pins.

	BOWLING										
	1	2	3	4	5	6	7	8	9	10	
TOM	7	9	6	8	7	9	6	5	6	4	67
SUE	7	8	4	9	9	5	7	8	9	5	71

My friend likes to
play basketball. I do, too!
We both like running
the ball up and down
the court. I want the ball
to go up, up, up into
the hoop so I will score.

TOM | SUE

10 | 14

Here we are playing ping-pong.
We both like ping-pong. We
try to keep the ball going.
I get to score when
my friend misses the ball.

TOM | SUE

Our last game is pool. I
have the red balls. I
will try to win the game
by getting all of my balls in
before my friend does.
I try not to get
the black ball in.
I will lose if it goes in.

TOM SUE
21   19

We are both winners!

	TOM	SUE
MINI GOLF	25	28
BASEBALL	2	3
BOWLING	67	71
BASKETBALL	10	14
TABLE TENNIS	5	3
POOL	21	19